BE YOURSELF

everyone ELSE IS already TAKEN

a guided JOURNAL FOR INTROSPECTION & SELF-*discovery*

THIS JOURNAL BELONGS TO:

_____

DATE: _____

KNOWING
YOURSELF
is
the
BEGINNING
of all
WISDOM

ARISTOTLE

HAPPY BIRTH DAY TO ME!

My birthdate: 1/12/98

Where I was born: CT

Who was present at my birth: mom & dad

My full birth name: Erin Kathleen Roach

Why my parents chose this name: My mom's sister always wanted an Erin and Kathleen is grandmother's name

This is what happened on the day of my birth: no idea everyone visited me!

like branches on a tree WE GROW in DIFFERENT DIRECTIONS YET OUR ROOTS REMAIN as ONE. Each of our lives will ALWAYS BE·A SPECIAL PART OF THE OTHER.

-UNKNOWN-

Family tree

Grandfather
Richard

Grandmother
Kathleen

Aunts & Uncles
Jeff
Kathy
Pattie

Mother
Nancy

Sisters
none

Grandfather	Grandmother
Tom II	Audrey

Father
Tom III

Aunts & Uncles
Brian
Peggy
Mary
Kathleen
Jane

Brothers
Sean &
Dylan

Me
Erin

Pets
Annie
Sammy
Murph
Sally
Callie

{Think about your childhood and the ways in which the members of your family helped shape who you are today. What occasions stand out in your mind when you think of each relative?}

The most memorable moments spent with my mom:

_____

_____

_____

_____

_____

_____

_____

_____

_____

_____

_____

_____

_____

Five words that describe my mom:

1. sensitive
2. loving
3.
4.
5.

The most memorable moments spent with my dad:

_____

_____

_____

_____

_____

_____

_____

_____

_____

_____

_____

_____

_____

_____

_____

Five words that describe my dad:

1. Kind
2. hardworking
3.
4.
5.

The most memorable moments spent with my siblings:

_____

_____

_____

_____

_____

_____

_____

_____

_____

_____

_____

_____

_____

_____

_____

_____

Five words that describe my siblings:

1.

2.

3.

4.

5.

The most memorable moments spent with my extended family or close family friends:

_____

_____

_____

_____

_____

_____

_____

_____

_____

_____

_____

_____

_____

_____

_____

_____

_____

_____

_____

_____

_____

_____

When my mom and dad describe what I was like
as a child, they usually say:

_____

_____

_____

_____

_____

_____

_____

_____

_____

_____

_____

_____

_____

_____

_____

_____

_____

_____

_____

_____

_____

_____

This is my favorite family tradition (and why):

_____

_____

_____

_____

_____

_____

_____

_____

_____

_____

_____

_____

_____

_____

_____

_____

_____

_____

_____

_____

_____

_____

_____

_____

the one charm of
the PAST
is that it is
the PAST

—oscar WILDE

My very earliest memory is from when
I was _____ years old. This is what I remember:

_____

_____

_____

_____

_____

_____

_____

_____

_____

_____

_____

_____

_____

_____

_____

_____

_____

_____

_____

_____

_____

_____

THESE ARE THE TIMES

DRAW A TIMELINE OF THE MEMORABLE EVENTS

YEAR: _____

YEAR: _____

YEAR: _____

YEAR: _____

YEAR: _____

YEAR: _____

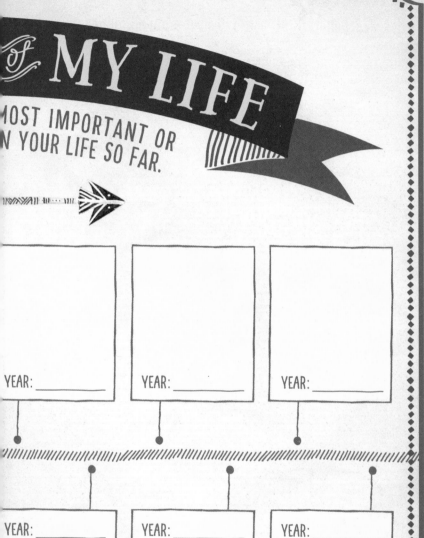

MY LIFE

MOST IMPORTANT OR
N YOUR LIFE SO FAR.

YEAR: _____

YEAR: _____

YEAR: _____

YEAR: _____

YEAR: _____

YEAR: _____

Generally. I would describe my childhood as:

_____

_____

_____

_____

_____

_____

_____

_____

_____

_____

_____

_____

_____

_____

_____

_____

_____

_____

_____

_____

_____

_____

_____

One of the happiest events in my childhood:

_____

_____

_____

_____

_____

_____

_____

_____

_____

_____

_____

_____

_____

_____

_____

_____

_____

_____

_____

_____

_____

_____

_____

_____

_____

One of the saddest events in my childhood:

_____

_____

_____

_____

_____

_____

_____

_____

_____

_____

_____

_____

_____

_____

_____

_____

_____

_____

_____

_____

_____

_____

_____

_____

A life-changing event of my childhood:

_____
_____
_____
_____
_____
_____
_____
_____
_____
_____
_____
_____
_____
_____
_____
_____
_____
_____
_____
_____
_____
_____
_____
_____
_____
_____
_____

My most memorable birthday:

_____
_____
_____
_____
_____
_____
_____
_____
_____
_____
_____
_____
_____
_____
_____
_____
_____
_____
_____
_____
_____
_____
_____
_____
_____

The most memorable holiday from my childhood:

_____

_____

_____

_____

_____

_____

_____

_____

_____

_____

_____

_____

_____

_____

_____

_____

_____

_____

_____

_____

_____

_____

_____

_____

OUR · GREATEST · GLORY

IS · NOT · IN
NEVER
FALLING
BUT · IN
RISING
EVERY · TIME · WE
FALL

OLIVER
GOLDSMITH

{Some memories aren't so happy, but they are still a part of you. Recall a time in your life when you learned a lesson the hard way or when you came out of a struggle with a new perspective.}

A mistake or bad decision I made that taught me an important lesson:

_____

_____

_____

_____

_____

_____

_____

_____

_____

_____

_____

_____

_____

_____

_____

_____

_____

_____

_____

_____

_____

When I was a child. I usually got in trouble for:

_____
_____
_____
_____
_____
_____
_____
_____
_____
_____
_____
_____

How I was usually punished:

_____
_____
_____
_____
_____
_____
_____
_____
_____
_____

How I felt about being punished:

_____

_____

_____

_____

_____

_____

_____

_____

_____

_____

_____

_____

_____

_____

_____

_____

_____

_____

_____

_____

_____

_____

_____

_____

INTELLIGENCE PLUS CHARACTER - that is the GOAL of true EDUCATION

MARTIN + LUTHER + KING + JR.

{Think about the schools you attended and the teachers you had throughout the years. Then briefly describe what you remember best about each year.}

Grade   Memory

_____

Grade   Memory

_____

Grade   Memory

_____

Grade   Memory

_____

Grade   Memory

_____

Grade   Memory

_____

Grade   Memory

_____

Grade   Memory

_____

Grade   Memory

_____

Grade   Memory

_____

Grade   Memory

_____

Grade   Memory

_____

Grade   Memory

_____

{Think back to your school days. Try to remember what those years were really like and how you felt about them at the time. Think about how things that happened in school might have affected who you are today.}

Things I liked about grade school
(favorite subjects/teachers/activities):

_____

_____

_____

_____

_____

_____

_____

_____

_____

_____

_____

_____

_____

_____

_____

_____

_____

_____

_____

_____

_____

Things I disliked about grade school
(least favorite subjects/teachers/activities):

_____

_____

_____

_____

_____

_____

_____

_____

_____

_____

_____

_____

_____

_____

_____

_____

_____

_____

_____

_____

Things I liked about high school
(favorite classes/teachers/activities):

_____

_____

_____

_____

_____

_____

_____

_____

_____

_____

_____

_____

_____

_____

_____

_____

_____

_____

_____

_____

_____

_____

_____

Things I disliked about high school
(least favorite classes/teachers/activities):

_____

_____

_____

_____

_____

_____

_____

_____

_____

_____

_____

_____

_____

_____

_____

_____

_____

_____

_____

_____

_____

_____

the ES·S·E·N·C·E of all RELIGIONS is ONE ONLY·THEIR APPROACHES ARE DIFFERENT.

MAHATMA·GANDHI

LEAP OF FAITH

{Describe the religious or spiritual beliefs—or lack thereof—you were raised with.}

_____

_____

_____

_____

_____

_____

_____

_____

_____

_____

_____

_____

_____

_____

_____

_____

_____

_____

_____

_____

_____

_____

_____

_____

_____

How I felt about religion and spirituality when I was a child:

_____

_____

_____

_____

_____

_____

_____

_____

_____

_____

_____

_____

_____

_____

_____

_____

_____

_____

_____

_____

_____

_____

_____

_____

How my views on religion and spirituality have evolved over time:

_____
_____
_____
_____
_____
_____
_____
_____
_____
_____
_____
_____
_____
_____
_____
_____
_____
_____
_____
_____
_____
_____
_____
_____
_____

A GOOD FRIEND

is hard to FIND, hard to LOSE, & hard to FORGET.

-UNKNOWN-

FRIENDSHIP WHEEL

Most Disappointing

Best

Most Inspiring

Most Entertaining

Most Unpredictable

Most Loyal

Most Unconventional

Most Honest

Worst Influence

Best Influence

The friend who had the most significant impact on my childhood:

Memories of good times I had with
my childhood friends:

_____

_____

_____

_____

_____

_____

_____

_____

_____

_____

_____

_____

_____

_____

_____

_____

_____

_____

_____

_____

_____

_____

_____

_____

_____

Memories of not-so-good times I had with my childhood friends:

_____
_____
_____
_____
_____
_____
_____
_____
_____
_____
_____
_____
_____
_____
_____
_____
_____
_____
_____
_____
_____
_____

One's FIRST LOVE is always PERFECT UNTIL one MEETS ONE'S SECOND LOVE

∘ELIZABETH∘ASTON∘

My first love was:

_____

A favorite memory from my first
romantic relationship:

_____

_____

_____

_____

_____

_____

_____

A past love who had the most significant impact
on who I am today (and why):

_____

_____

_____

_____

_____

_____

_____

_____

You have to kiss a lot of frogs before you meet Prince Charming. Here are some "frogs" from my past:

_____

_____

_____

_____

These imperfect relationships allowed me to emerge as a better person by:

_____

_____

_____

_____

_____

_____

_____

If I could erase one relationship from my past, it would be (and why):

_____

_____

_____

_____

_____

_____

My first heartbreak was with:

_____

Something positive that came out of it:

_____

_____

_____

_____

_____

_____

_____

If I could give relationship advice to my
younger self, I would say:

_____

_____

_____

_____

_____

_____

_____

Not all those who wander are lost

J.R.R. Tolkien

The most memorable trip I have ever taken was:

_____

_____

My favorite part of the journey was:

_____

_____

_____

_____

_____

_____

_____

_____

How I grew from this experience:

_____

_____

_____

_____

_____

_____

_____

{Think about a time when you returned from a trip. Did you feel like you didn't belong in your old life anymore? What foreign customs or traditions that you observed did you yearn to experience at home? What did you miss most about home? Explain.}

{Do you think it is important to travel and explore other lifestyles and cultures? Why or why not?}

_____

_____

_____

_____

_____

_____

_____

_____

_____

_____

_____

_____

_____

_____

_____

_____

_____

_____

_____

_____

_____

THE · FIRST · TO · APOLOGIZE · IS · THE

Bravest.

THE · FIRST · TO · FORGIVE · IS · THE

Strongest.

THE · FIRST · TO · FORGET · IS · THE

Happiest.

Forgiveness is an important part of living a peaceful, fulfilling life. The person that was hardest to forgive in my life so far:

_____

_____

What this person did:

_____

_____

_____

_____

_____

_____

_____

_____

_____

_____

_____

How forgiving this person made me feel:

_____

_____

_____

_____

It is often difficult to say, "I'm sorry." In my life,
it was most difficult to apologize to:

_____

_____

What I did:

_____

_____

_____

_____

_____

_____

_____

_____

_____

_____

_____

_____

How apologizing to this person made me feel:

_____

_____

_____

A friend or family member whom
I still need to forgive (and why):

_____

_____

_____

_____

_____

_____

_____

_____

_____

_____

A friend or family member who still deserves
an apology from me (and why):

_____

_____

_____

_____

_____

_____

_____

_____

_____

_____

_____

{Recall a time when you wanted to be like somebody else. Think about why you admired this person and what specific qualities you desired to emulate.}

The person I once admired most:

_____

_____

Why I admired this person:

_____

_____

_____

_____

_____

_____

_____

_____

_____

_____

What I learned about myself from this experience:

_____

_____

_____

_____

_____

_____

_____

When I was younger I was:

- ☐ Angry
- ☐ Athletic
- ☐ Boisterous
- ☐ Bold
- ☐ Bratty
- ☐ Bright
- ☐ Cheerful
- ☐ Clever
- ☐ Confident
- ☐ Considerate
- ☐ Creative
- ☐ Daring
- ☐ Disobedient
- ☐ Dramatic
- ☐ Eager
- ☐ Easygoing
- ☐ Emotional
- ☐ Empathetic
- ☐ Energetic
- ☐ Feisty
- ☐ Foolish
- ☐ Forgetful

- ☐ Friendly
- ☐ Funny
- ☐ Gullible
- ☐ Happy
- ☐ Helpful
- ☐ Honest
- ☐ Hopeful
- ☐ Hyper
- ☐ Imaginative
- ☐ Impatient
- ☐ Impulsive
- ☐ Independent
- ☐ Insecure
- ☐ Introspective
- ☐ Kind
- ☐ Loving
- ☐ Moody
- ☐ Naive
- ☐ Naughty
- ☐ Needy
- ☐ Obedient
- ☐ Opinionated

- ☐ Optimistic
- ☐ Outgoing
- ☐ Outspoken
- ☐ Passionate
- ☐ Pensive
- ☐ Pessimistic
- ☐ Quiet
- ☐ Quirky
- ☐ Reckless
- ☐ Respectful
- ☐ Sad
- ☐ Sensitive
- ☐ Shy
- ☐ Smart
- ☐ Stubborn
- ☐ Talkative
- ☐ Thoughtful
- ☐ Wild
- ☐ Withdrawn
- ☐ _____
- ☐ _____
- ☐ _____

{Think about "nature versus nurture" in regards to personality. Were you born with your personality, or did you acquire it through time and experiences? Explain.}

{Draw a map of your personality. Include all significant factors that have contributed to who you are. How has your personality changed since you were younger? Which traits have been consistent since birth? Which traits are ever-changing, influenced daily by the people and events you encounter?}

If I could go back in time and offer advice to my younger self. I would say:

_____

_____

_____

_____

_____

_____

_____

_____

_____

_____

_____

_____

_____

_____

_____

_____

_____

_____

_____

_____

_____

_____

_____

TODAY
YOU
YOU are THAT is
TRUER than TRUE.
there is
NO ALIVE
one
who is
YOUER
than YOU
-DR- SEUSS

CHAPTER

2

THE HERE & NOW

WHO *You* ARE *Today*

Three names I go by:

1. _____
2. _____
3. _____

Three places I've visited:

1. _____
2. _____
3. _____

Three TV shows I watch:

1. _____
2. _____
3. _____

Three books I've read:

1. _____
2. _____
3. _____

Three things I like to do:

1. _____
2. _____
3. _____

Three places I like to shop:

1. _____
2. _____
3. _____

Three of my favorite drinks:

1. _____
2. _____
3. _____

Three of my favorite words:

1. _____
2. _____
3. _____

Three things I look forward to:

1. _____
2. _____
3. _____

Three of my favorite foods:

1. _____
2. _____
3. _____

{Explain yourself in a nutshell. What are some words or phrases that best describe your personality?}

I would describe my personal style as:

_____

_____

_____

_____

_____

The biggest influence on my style:

_____

_____

_____

_____

_____

_____

I want my style to convey:

_____

_____

_____

_____

_____

_____

_____

_____

These are my quirks:

_____

_____

_____

_____

_____

_____

_____

_____

_____

_____

_____

What I think these quirks reveal about me:

_____

_____

_____

_____

_____

_____

_____

_____

i don't have

PET-PEEVES

i have whole

KENNELS

of **IRRITATION**

WHOOPI GOLDBERG

My pet peeves:

_____

_____

_____

_____

_____

_____

_____

_____

_____

_____

_____

_____

What I think these pet peeves reveal about me:

_____

_____

_____

_____

_____

_____

_____

_____

These are my greatest fears, listed from most significant to least significant:

_____

_____

_____

_____

_____

_____

_____

_____

_____

_____

_____

_____

_____

_____

_____

_____

_____

_____

_____

_____

_____

_____

_____

_____

A fear I believe I could overcome if given the opportunity: _____

_____

_____

Things I feared as a child that I don't fear now: _____

_____

_____

_____

_____

_____

_____

Things I fear now that I didn't fear as a child: _____

_____

_____

_____

_____

_____

_____

A fear I believe will always be with me: _____

_____

_____

_____

Things that make me feel alive:

_____

_____

_____

_____

_____

_____

_____

_____

_____

_____

_____

_____

_____

_____

_____

_____

_____

_____

_____

_____

_____

_____

_____

Things that I love:

Things that make me laugh:

YOU'RE *Always* WITH·YOURSELF, SO·YOU·MIGHT·AS·WELL *Enjoy* the COMPANY

=DIANE·VON·FURSTENBERG=

Ten things I like about myself:

1. _____

2. _____

3. _____

4. _____

5. _____

6. _____

7. _____

8. _____

9. _____

10. _____

Three things I'd like to improve about myself:

1.

2.

3.

Something that very few people know about me:

_____

_____

_____

_____

_____

_____

Something my parents would be surprised
to learn about me:

_____

_____

_____

_____

_____

_____

Something my best friend would be surprised
to learn about me:

_____

_____

_____

_____

_____

_____

Three qualities of mine that others often compliment:

1. _____

_____

2. _____

_____

3. _____

_____

Three qualities of mine that others sometimes complain about:

1. _____

_____

2. _____

_____

3. _____

_____

What I value most in life:

_____
_____
_____
_____
_____
_____
_____
_____
_____
_____

What I value most in people:

_____
_____
_____
_____
_____
_____
_____
_____
_____
_____
_____
_____

the TIME is ALWAYS RIGHT to DO WHAT IS RIGHT.

-MARTIN LUTHER KING JR.-

{According to ancient Greek philosophy, the four Cardinal virtues of moral excellence are prudence, justice, temperance, and courage. Think about these virtues and how they relate to your own moral framework. Write about how you exhibit each in your own life and how you could better yourself by thinking of these virtues from time to time.}

Prudence (common sense):

_____

_____

_____

_____

_____

_____

_____

_____

_____

Justice:

_____

_____

_____

_____

_____

_____

_____

_____

_____

Temperance (self-control):

_____

_____

_____

_____

_____

_____

_____

_____

_____

Courage:

_____

_____

_____

_____

_____

_____

_____

_____

_____

_____

_____

When I have time to myself, I often
reflect on these topics:

_____
_____
_____
_____
_____
_____
_____
_____
_____
_____
_____
_____
_____
_____
_____
_____
_____
_____
_____
_____
_____
_____
_____

I try to make the world a better place by:

_____
_____
_____
_____
_____
_____
_____
_____
_____
_____
_____
_____
_____
_____
_____
_____
_____
_____
_____
_____
_____
_____
_____
_____

I consider myself to be a(n):

☐ Optimist   ☐ Pessimist

I am generally optimistic about: _____

_____

_____

_____

_____

_____

_____

I am generally pessimistic about: _____

_____

_____

_____

_____

_____

_____

How my pessimism affects my life: _____

_____

_____

_____

_____

_____

Five positive changes I can make
in my life right now:

1. _____

_____

_____

2. _____

_____

_____

3. _____

_____

_____

4. _____

_____

_____

5. _____

_____

_____

Go confidently in the direction of your DREAMS LIVE THE LIFE YOU·HAVE IMAGINED

HENRY DAVID THOREAU

My current job is: _____

_____

_____

_____

_____

My dream job is: _____

_____

_____

_____

_____

My nightmare job is: _____

_____

_____

_____

_____

If all occupations paid equally and job satisfaction were
the only consideration, I would be: _____

_____

_____

_____

_____

_____

{Circle one of the two choices in each prompt below: then explain.}

I would rather work alone.
I would rather work in a group.

_____

_____

_____

_____

_____

I would rather lead.
I would rather follow.

_____

_____

_____

_____

_____

_____

I would rather be a teacher.
I would rather be a student.

_____

_____

_____

_____

_____

The option that best describes my working style is:

- ☐ I immediately begin working on an assignment after it is given to me and usually finish long before it is due.

- ☐ Slow and steady wins the race. I work in stages—a little bit of work, a short break. But I always finish on time.

- ☐ I work best under pressure. I wait until the day before something is due; then I get to work and power through it, usually finishing on time.

- ☐ I ask for an extension, and then I might finish the assignment. Later.

I can improve my working style (or reduce my stress) by:

_____

_____

_____

_____

_____

_____

_____

_____

_____

My biggest distractions are:

_____
_____
_____
_____
_____
_____
_____
_____
_____
_____

My biggest motivators are:

_____
_____
_____
_____
_____
_____
_____
_____
_____
_____
_____
_____

Things that help me focus:

_____
_____
_____
_____
_____
_____
_____
_____
_____
_____
_____
_____
_____
_____
_____
_____
_____
_____
_____
_____
_____
_____
_____
_____
_____
_____

Good Friends are like STARS.

You don't always see them, but you know they're Always THERE.

BECCA CAHAN

Five people that I am grateful for today:

1. _____

2. _____

3. _____

4. _____

5. _____

Five important qualities in a friend:

1. _____

2. _____

3. _____

4. _____

5. _____

I would rather have:

☐ One extremely close best friend

☐ Many moderately close casual friends

The friend who encourages me most: _____

_____

The friend who always lends a shoulder to cry on: _____

_____

The friend who listens best: _____

_____

The friend who gives the best advice: _____

_____

The friend who always makes me laugh: _____

_____

The friend who can keep a secret: _____

_____

The friend who is most inspiring to me: _____

_____

The friend who is most loyal: _____

_____

The three most reliable people
in my "pit crew":

1.

2.

3.

How my friends would describe me:

_____

_____

_____

_____

_____

_____

How I would describe myself as
a friend to others:

_____

_____

_____

_____

_____

_____

_____

Three qualities I would like to cultivate within
myself to become a better friend:

1.

2.

3.

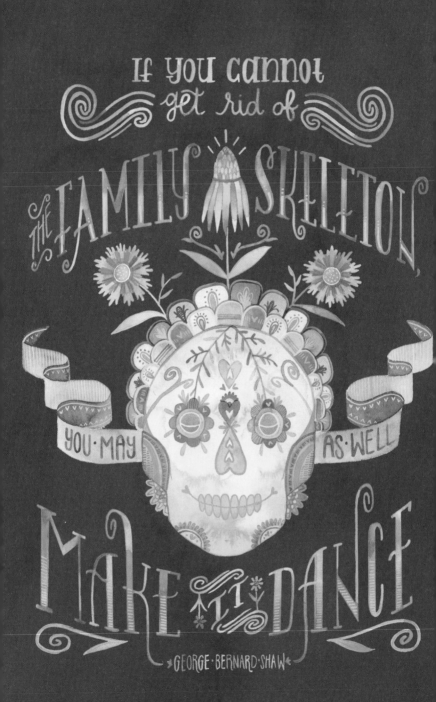

How my family members would describe me:

_____

_____

_____

_____

_____

_____

How these descriptions are different from
the way I perceive myself:

_____

_____

_____

_____

_____

_____

Five words that describe my family:

1.

2.

3.

4.

5.

A relative who is most like a friend (and why): _____

_____

_____

_____

_____

A relative I admire most (and why): _____

_____

_____

_____

_____

A relative I would like to get to know better (and why):

_____

_____

_____

_____

_____

A relative I struggle to connect with (and why): _____

_____

_____

_____

_____

_____

The ways I am like my family:

_____
_____
_____
_____
_____
_____
_____
_____
_____

The ways I am not like my family:

_____
_____
_____
_____
_____
_____
_____
_____
_____
_____
_____

{Think about what makes someone beautiful—both inside and out.
Fill in the acrostic below with words that describe your kind of beautiful.}

B _____

E _____

A _____

U _____

T _____

I _____

F _____

U _____

L _____

THAT'S THE WAY LOVE GOES

{Rate the following factors according to your preference for them in a mate. 0 = not important. 1 = somewhat important. 2 = important. and 3 = extremely important.}

_____ Age		_____ Income
_____ Ambition		_____ Intelligence
_____ Baggage (or lack thereof)		_____ Kindness
_____ Dance moves		_____ Looks
_____ Education		_____ Manners
_____ Family-approved		_____ Physical chemistry
_____ Friend-approved		_____ Religion
_____ Generosity		_____ Romantic gestures
_____ Good with animals		_____ Sense of humor
_____ Good with kids		_____ Similar interests
_____ Hair (or lack thereof)		_____ Similar values
_____ Honesty/Integrity		_____ Style
_____ Height/Weight		_____ Work ethic

Characteristics that make someone lovable:

_____
_____
_____
_____
_____
_____
_____
_____
_____
_____
_____
_____

Characteristics that make someone difficult to love:

_____
_____
_____
_____
_____
_____
_____
_____
_____
_____
_____

These are the things that make me a "good catch":

_____

_____

_____

_____

_____

_____

_____

_____

_____

_____

Things a secret admirer could do to get my attention:

_____

_____

_____

_____

_____

_____

_____

_____

_____

_____

_____

How my idea of a successful romantic
relationship has evolved over time:

_____

_____

_____

_____

_____

_____

_____

_____

_____

The scariest part about falling in love is:

_____

_____

_____

_____

_____

_____

_____

_____

_____

_____

time you ENJOY WASTING is not WASTED TIME

MARTHE TROLY-CURTIN

I enjoy wasting time by:

My ideal night out with friends:

My ideal night in by myself:

_____
_____
_____
_____
_____
_____
_____
_____
_____
_____
_____
_____
_____
_____
_____
_____
_____
_____
_____
_____
_____
_____

Keep Calm and...

☐ Call a friend   ☐ Make cookies

☐ Dance   ☐ Meditate

☐ Do yoga   ☐ Pet a dog

☐ Drink tea   ☐ Play with a cat

☐ Eat chocolate   ☐ Read a book

☐ Get a facial   ☐ Sing in the shower

☐ Get a mani/pedi   ☐ Surf the Internet

☐ Get a massage   ☐ Take a bubble bath

☐ Go for a run   ☐ Take a nap

☐ Go shopping   ☐ Take a walk

☐ Hug a tree   ☐ Watch a movie

☐ Kiss a baby   ☐ Write it all down

☐ Listen to music   ☐ _____

☐ Make art   ☐ _____

How I generally direct my extra energy:

- ☐ Cleaning
- ☐ Cooking
- ☐ Crafting
- ☐ Creating art
- ☐ Eating or drinking
- ☐ Exercising
- ☐ Gaming
- ☐ Helping people
- ☐ Loving

- ☐ Organizing
- ☐ Planning for the future
- ☐ Playing sports
- ☐ Reading
- ☐ Reflecting
- ☐ Volunteering
- ☐ Working
- ☐ Writing
- ☐ _____

How I would prefer to direct my extra energy:

_____

_____

_____

_____

_____

_____

_____

_____

Medicine
HEALS THE BODY
MUSIC HEALS
THE Soul

My favorite female singer: _____

My favorite male singer: _____

My favorite band: _____

My favorite music video: _____

A song that reminds me of home: _____

A song I listen to when I'm sad: _____

A song that motivates me: _____

A song that calms me down: _____

A song that inspires me: _____

A song that makes me think: _____

A song that makes me cry: _____

A song I sing aloud when I'm alone: _____

A song I've heard too many times: _____

If my life were a song, it would be called: _____

_____

My most important short-term goals:

_____

_____

_____

_____

_____

_____

_____

_____

_____

_____

How I plan to achieve these goals:

_____

_____

_____

_____

_____

_____

_____

_____

_____

_____

_____

_____

My most important long-term goals:

_____

_____

_____

_____

_____

_____

_____

_____

_____

How I plan to achieve these goals:

_____

_____

_____

_____

_____

_____

_____

_____

_____

_____

_____

Places I want to visit:

_____
_____
_____
_____
_____
_____
_____
_____
_____
_____
_____

Activities I want to try:

_____
_____
_____
_____
_____
_____
_____
_____
_____
_____
_____
_____
_____

Skills I want to acquire:

_____
_____
_____
_____
_____
_____
_____
_____
_____
_____

Things I want to learn:

_____
_____
_____
_____
_____
_____
_____
_____
_____
_____
_____
_____

This is how I envision my dream wedding:

_____

_____

_____

_____

_____

_____

_____

_____

_____

_____

_____

_____

_____

_____

_____

_____

_____

_____

_____

_____

_____

_____

_____

_____

This is how I envision my dream honeymoon:

_____
_____
_____
_____
_____
_____
_____
_____
_____
_____
_____
_____
_____
_____
_____
_____
_____
_____
_____
_____
_____
_____
_____
_____
_____

MY FUTURE FAMILY

My ideal number of children:

Boys _____

Girls _____

Potential boy names:

_____   _____

_____   _____

_____   _____

_____   _____

_____   _____

_____   _____

_____   _____

_____   _____

Potential girl names:

_____   _____

_____   _____

_____   _____

_____   _____

_____   _____

_____   _____

_____   _____

_____   _____

Pets I would like to have:

- ☐ Bird
- ☐ Cat
- ☐ Chameleon
- ☐ Chinchilla
- ☐ Dog
- ☐ Donkey
- ☐ Ferret
- ☐ Fish
- ☐ Frog
- ☐ Gecko
- ☐ Gerbil
- ☐ Goat
- ☐ Guinea Pig
- ☐ Hamster

- ☐ Hermit Crab
- ☐ Horse
- ☐ Iguana
- ☐ Lizard
- ☐ Mouse
- ☐ Pony
- ☐ Pot-Bellied Pig
- ☐ Rabbit
- ☐ Rat
- ☐ Snake
- ☐ Tarantula
- ☐ Tortoise
- ☐ Turtle
- ☐ _____

Types and potential names of pets:

_____

_____

_____

_____

_____

_____

_____

_____

The style of my dream home would be:

- ☐ Art Deco
- ☐ Beach House
- ☐ Brownstone
- ☐ Cape Cod
- ☐ Castle
- ☐ Colonial Revival
- ☐ Contemporary
- ☐ Craftsman Bungalow
- ☐ Farm House
- ☐ Igloo
- ☐ Log Cabin

- ☐ Mansion
- ☐ Mediterranean
- ☐ Mid-20th Century
- ☐ Ranch House
- ☐ Spanish
- ☐ Tree House
- ☐ Tudor Revival
- ☐ Tuscan
- ☐ Victorian
- ☐ Zen
- ☐ _____

My dream home is in or near the:

- ☐ Beach
- ☐ City
- ☐ Countryside
- ☐ Desert

- ☐ Forest
- ☐ Mountains
- ☐ Suburbs
- ☐ _____

Must-have features in my dream home:

SOMETIMES things become POSSIBLE if we WANT them BAD·ENOUGH

T·S·ELIOT

If I were presented with a time machine.
I would take it to:

_____

_____

While there. I would:

_____

_____

_____

_____

_____

_____

_____

_____

_____

_____

_____

_____

_____

_____

_____

_____

_____

_____

If a magic genie granted me three wishes,
I would wish for:

1. _____
_____
_____
_____
_____
_____

2. _____
_____
_____
_____
_____
_____

3. _____
_____
_____
_____
_____
_____

If I were stranded on a desert island and could
take only three things with me, I'd take:

1. _____

2. _____

3. _____

If I could choose one person to be there
with me, I would choose:

_____

What I would miss most about
my current life:

_____

_____

_____

_____

_____

_____

_____

_____

_____

_____

_____

_____

_____

If I strike it rich in the lottery, I will:

If I could invite three famous people (living or dead) to dinner. I would invite:

1.

2.

3.

Why I chose these people:

_____

_____

_____

_____

_____

_____

_____

_____

_____

_____

_____

_____

_____

_____

_____

_____

If I could have any superpower it would be:

_____

_____

The name of my superhero alter-ego would be:

_____

_____

Things I would do with my superpower:

_____

_____

_____

_____

_____

_____

_____

_____

_____

_____

_____

_____

_____

_____

_____

_____

If my life were a movie, it would be called:

_____

The movie would be rated:

_____

_____ would play me.

_____ would play my best friend.

_____ would play my significant other.

_____ would play my mom.

_____ would play my dad.

_____ would play _____

_____ would play _____

_____ would write the soundtrack.

People I would thank in my Academy Award
acceptance speech:

_____

_____

_____

_____

_____

_____

_____

_____

_____

THE PURPOSE OF
= life =
IS·NOT·TO·BE·HAPPY·IT·IS

TO BE USEFUL TO BE HONORABLE

TO BE COMPASSIONATE

TO HAVE IT MAKE SOME DIFFERENCE

THAT·YOU·HAVE·LIVED·AND
= lived =
WELL
=RALPH WALDO EMERSON=

How I will be useful:

How I will be honorable:

How I will be compassionate:

How I will make a difference:

_____

_____

_____

_____

_____

_____

_____

_____

_____

_____

_____

_____

_____

_____

_____

_____

_____

_____

_____

_____

_____

_____

_____

_____

_____

_____

_____

_____

If I had the option to relive my entire life,
I would choose to:

_____
_____
_____
_____
_____

I would most want to relive:

_____
_____
_____
_____
_____
_____
_____

I would least want to relive:

_____
_____
_____
_____
_____
_____
_____

Some of the things I would do differently:

_____

_____

_____

_____

_____

_____

_____

_____

_____

_____

_____

_____

_____

_____

_____

_____

_____

_____

_____

_____

_____

_____

_____

I believe in myself because:

_____

_____

_____

_____

_____

_____

_____

_____

_____

_____

_____

_____

_____

_____

_____

_____

_____

_____

_____

_____

_____

_____

_____

_____

One word to describe the person I WAS:

_____

One word to describe the person I AM:

_____

One word to describe the person I WILL BE:

_____

{Place a photo of yourself here.}